100 No1 Hits

Exclusive Distributors:
Music Sales Limited
8/9 Frith Street,
London W1V 5TZ, England.
Music Sales Pty Limited
120 Rothschild Avenue,
Rosebery, NSW 2018,
Australia.

This book © Copyright 1993
by Wise Publications
Order No.AM90130
ISBN 0-7119-3192-5

Book design by Studio Twenty, London
Compiled by Peter Evans
Music arranged by Peter Lavender
Music processed by MSS Studios

Music Sales' complete catalogue lists thousands of titles and is
free from your local music shop, or direct from Music Sales Limited.
Please send a cheque/postal order for £1.50 for postage to:
Music Sales Limited, Newmarket Road, Bury St. Edmunds, Suffolk IP33 3YB.

Printed in the United Kingdom by
Redwood Books, Trowbridge, Wiltshire.

Wise Publications
London/New York/Paris/Sydney/Copenhagen/Madrid

A Good Heart *Feargal Sharkey* 107
16 November 1985 (2 weeks)

A Hard Day's Night *The Beatles* 20
23 July 1964 (3 weeks)

A Whiter Shade Of Pale *Procol Harum* 36
8 June 1967 (3 weeks)

A Woman In Love *Barbra Streisand* 100
25 October 1980 (3 weeks)

All I Have To Do Is Dream *Everly Brothers* 9
4 July 1958 (7 weeks)

All You Need Is Love *The Beatles* 38
19 July 1967 (3 weeks)

Always On My Mind *Pet Shop Boys* 125
19 December 1987 (4 weeks)

Amazing Grace *The Royal Scots Dragoon Guards* 54
15 April 1972 (5 weeks)

Annie's Song *John Denver* 60
12 October 1974 (1 week)

Anyone Who Had A Heart *Cilla Black* 14
27 February 1964 (3 weeks)

Bridge Over Troubled Water *Simon & Garfunkel* 50
28 March 1970 (3 weeks)

Bright Eyes *Art Garfunkel* 88
14 April 1979 (6 weeks)

Can't Buy Me Love *The Beatles* 16
2 April 1964 (3 weeks)

Clair *Gilbert O'Sullivan* 56
11 November 1972 (2 weeks)

Claudette *Everly Brothers* 8
4 July 1958 (7 weeks)

Dancing Queen *Abba* 74
4 September 1976 (6 weeks)

Don't Cry For Me Argentina *Julie Covington* 78
17 February 1977 (1 week)

Don't Stand So Close To Me *Police* 98
27 September 1980 (4 weeks)

Ebony And Ivory *Paul McCartney & Stevie Wonder* 108
24 April 1982 (3 weeks)

Eternal Flame *The Bangles* 142
15 April 1989 (4 weeks)

Every Breath You Take *Police* 112
4 June 1983 (4 weeks)

(Everything I Do) I Do It For You *Bryan Adams* 148
13 July 1991 (16 weeks)

Fernando *Abba* 72
8 May 1976 (4 weeks)

Get Off Of My Cloud *The Rolling Stones* 27
4 November 1965 (3 weeks)

Glad All Over *Dave Clark Five* 13
16 January 1964 (2 weeks)

Gonna Make You A Star *David Essex* 64
14 November 1974 (3 weeks)

Good Vibrations *Beach Boys* 32
17 November 1966 (2 weeks)

Goodnight Girl *Wet Wet Wet* 150
19 January 1992 (4 weeks)

Green, Green Grass Of Home *Tom Jones* 33
1 December 1966 (7 weeks)

Hangin' Tough *New Kids On The Block* 137
13 January 1990 (2 weeks)

He Ain't Heavy He's My Brother *The Hollies* 135
24 September 1988 (2 weeks)

Hello Goodbye *The Beatles* 40
6 December 1967 (6 weeks)

Help! *The Beatles* 26
5 August 1965 (3 weeks)

Hey Jude *The Beatles* 45
11 September 1968 (2 weeks)

I Can't Stop Loving You *Ray Charles* 11
12 July 1962 (2 weeks)

I Feel Fine *The Beatles* 17
10 December 1964 (5 weeks)

I Know Him So Well *Barbara Dickson & Elaine Paige* 116
9 February 1985 (4 weeks)

I Think We're Alone Now *Tiffany* 134
30 January 1988 (3 weeks)

I Wanna Dance With Somebody (Who Loves Me) *Whitney Houston* 130
6 June 1987 (2 weeks)

I Want To Wake Up With You *Boris Gardiner* 124
23 August 1986 (3 weeks)

I Will Survive *Gloria Gaynor* 86
17 March 1979 (4 weeks)

I'd Like To Teach The World To Sing *The New Seekers* 47
8 January 1972 (4 weeks)

I'm Not In Love *10CC* 68
28 June 1975 (2 weeks)

I've Got To Get A Message To You *Bee Gees* 44
4 September 1968 (1 week)

If You Leave Me Now *Chicago* 76
16 October 1976 (3 weeks)

Imagine *John Lennon* 104
10 January 1981 (4 weeks)

It's Over *Roy Orbison* 18
25 June 1964 (2 weeks)

Itsy Bitsy, Teenie Weenie, Yellow Polkadot Bikini *Bombalurina* 144
25 August 1990 (3 weeks)

Jealous Guy *Roxy Music* 105
14 March 1981 (2 weeks)

Jumpin' Jack Flash *The Rolling Stones* 43
19 June 1968 (2 weeks)

(Just Like) Starting Over *John Lennon* 102
20 December 1980 (1 week)

Keep On Running *Spencer Davis Group* 28
20 January 1966 (1 week)

Knowing Me, Knowing You *Abba* 67
2 April 1977 (5 weeks)

The Lady In Red *Chris De Burgh* 128
2 August 1986 (3 weeks)

Lady Madonna *The Beatles* 42
27 March 1968 (2 weeks)

Mamma Mia *Abba* 70
31 January 1976 (2 weeks)

Massachusetts *Bee Gees* 37
10 October 1967 (4 weeks)

Memories Are Made Of This *Dean Martin* 6
17 February 1956 (4 weeks)

Merry Xmas Everybody *Slade* 62
15 December 1973 (5 weeks)

Message In A Bottle *Police* 92
29 September 1979 (3 weeks)

Mistletoe And Wine *Cliff Richard* 136
10 December 1988 (4 weeks)

Mr Tambourine Man *Byrds* 25
25 July 1965 (2 weeks)

Mull Of Kintyre *Wings* 82
3 December 1977 (9 weeks)

Ob-La-Di, Ob-La-Da *Marmalade* 48
1 January 1969 (1 week) & 15 January 1969 (2 weeks)

Oh, Pretty Woman *Roy Orbison* 22
8 October 1964 (2 weeks) & 12 November 1964 (1 week)

One Moment In Time *Whitney Houston* 138
15 October 1988 (2 weeks)

Only The Lonely *Roy Orbison* 10
20 October 1960 (2 weeks)

Paint It Black *The Rolling Stones* 29
26 May 1966 (1 week)

Paperback Writer *The Beatles* 31
23 June 1966 (2 weeks)

Pipes Of Peace *Paul McCartney* 114
14 January 1984 (2 weeks)

The Power Of Love *Jennifer Rush* 120
12 October 1985 (5 weeks)

Release Me *Engelbert Humperdinck* 34
2 March 1967 (6 weeks)

Rock Around The Clock *Bill Haley & His Comets* 4
25 November 1955 (3 weeks) & 6 January 1956 (2 weeks)

Sailing *Rod Stewart* 66
6 September 1975 (4 weeks)

Save Your Love *Renée & Renato* 110
18 December 1982 (4 weeks)

Saviour's Day *Cliff Richard* 146
29 December 1990 (1 week)

Sixteen Tons *Tennessee Ernie Ford* 5
20 January 1956 (4 weeks)

Somethin' Stupid *Frank & Nancy Sinatra* 35
13 April 1967 (2 weeks)

Something's Gotten Hold Of My Heart *Marc Almond & Gene Pitney* 140
28 January 1989 (4 weeks)

Spirit In The Sky *Norman Greenbaum* 52
2 May 1970 (2 weeks)

Strangers In The Night *Frank Sinatra* 30
2 June 1966 (3 weeks)

Telstar *Tornados* 12
4 October 1962 (5 weeks)

That'll Be The Day *Crickets* 7
1 November 1957 (3 weeks)

There Must Be An Angel (Playing With My Heart) *Eurythmics* 118
27 July 1985 (1 week)

(This Could Be) The Last Time *The Rolling Stones* 24
18 March 1965 (3 weeks)

This Ole House *Shakin' Stevens* 106
28 March 1981 (3 weeks)

Those Were The Days *Mary Hopkin* 46
25 September 1968 (6 weeks)

Tie A Yellow Ribbon 'Round The Ole Oak Tree *Dawn* 58
21 April 1973 (4 weeks)

Tragedy *Bee Gees* 84
3 March 1979 (2 weeks)

Unchained Melody *Righteous Brothers* 145
3 November 1990 (4 weeks)

Uptown Girl *Billy Joel* 122
5 November 1983 (5 weeks)

Walking On The Moon *Police* 81
8 December 1979 (1 week)

We Don't Talk Anymore *Cliff Richard* 90
25 August 1979 (4 weeks)

Welcome Home (Vivre) *Peters & Lee* 55
21 July 1973 (1 week)

What's Another Year? *Johnny Logan* 94
17 May 1980 (2 weeks)

When The Going Gets Tough, The Tough Get Going *Billy Ocean* 126
8 February 1986 (4 weeks)

Whispering Grass *Windsor Davies & Don Estelle* 61
7 June 1975 (3 weeks)

The Winner Takes It All *Abba* 96
9 August 1980 (2 weeks)

YMCA *Village People* 80
6 January 1979 (3 weeks)

You Win Again *Bee Gees* 132
17 October 1987 (4 weeks)

Rock Around The Clock

Words & Music by Max C. Freedman & Jimmy de Knight

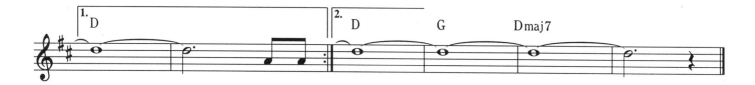

Sixteen Tons

Words & Music by Merle Travis

Moderately

Memories Are Made Of This

Words & Music by Terry Gilkyson, Richard Dehr & Frank Miller

That'll Be The Day

Words & Music by Norman Petty, Buddy Holly & Jerry Allison

Claudette

Words & Music by Roy Orbison

Moderately

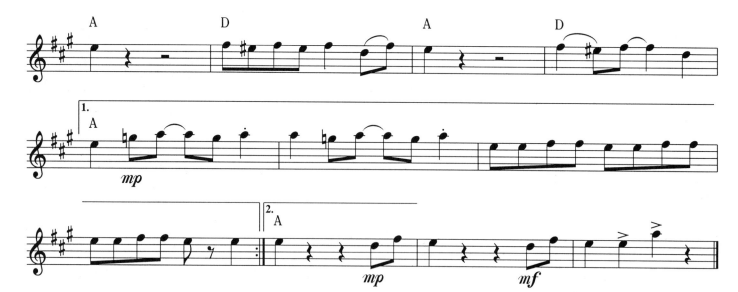

All I Have To Do Is Dream

Words & Music by Boudleaux Bryant

Only The Lonely

Words & Music by Roy Orbison & Joe Melson

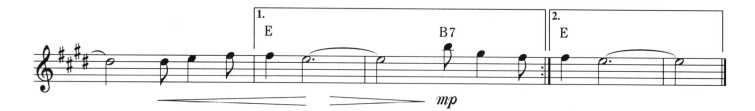

I Can't Stop Loving You

Words & Music by Don Gibson

Telstar

Composed by Joe Meek

Glad All Over

Words & Music by Dave Clark & Mike Smith

Anyone Who Had A Heart

Words by Hal David. Music by Burt Bacharach

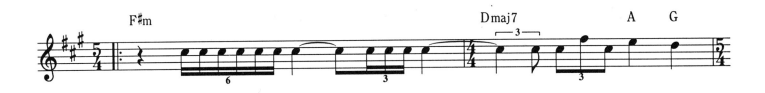

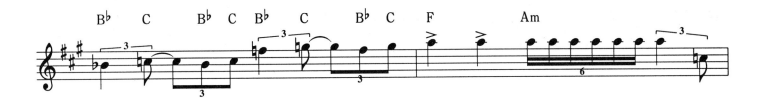

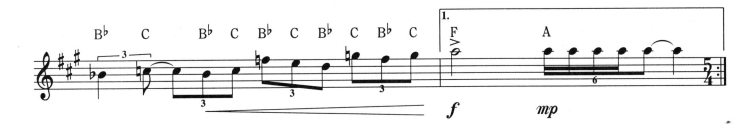

Can't Buy Me Love

Words & Music by John Lennon & Paul McCartney

I Feel Fine

Words & Music by John Lennon & Paul McCartney

Moderately

⊕ Coda

It's Over

Words & Music by Roy Orbison & Bill Dees

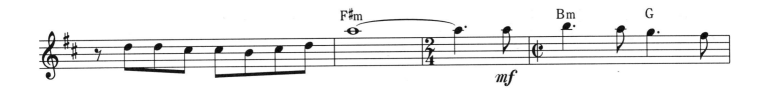

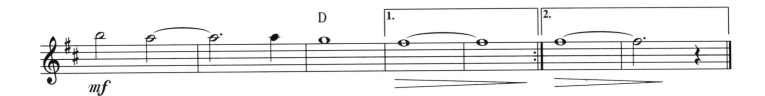

A Hard Days Night

Words & Music by John Lennon & Paul McCartney

Moderately, with a beat

⊕ Coda

Oh, Pretty Woman

Words & Music by Roy Orbison & Bill Dees

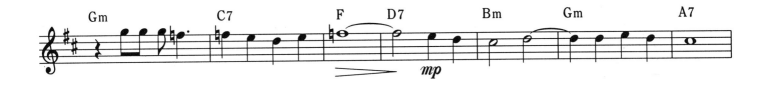

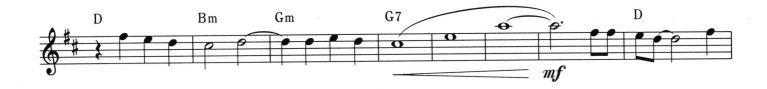

This Could Be The Last Time

Words & Music by Mick Jagger & Keith Richards

Mr. Tambourine Man

Words & Music by Bob Dylan

Help!

Words & Music by John Lennon & Paul McCartney

Get Off Of My Cloud

Words & Music by Mick Jagger & Keith Richards

Keep On Running

Words & Music by Jackie Edwards

Paint It Black

Words & Music by Mick Jagger & Keith Richards

Strangers In The Night

Words by Charles Singleton & Eddie Snyder. Music by Bert Kaempfert

Beguine tempo

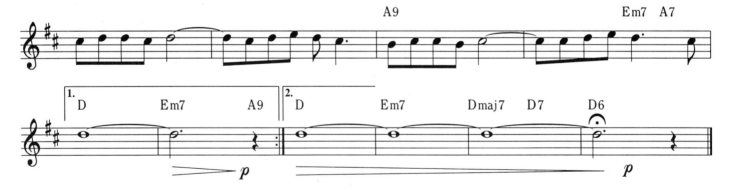

Paperback Writer

Words & Music by John Lennon & Paul McCartney

Good Vibrations

Words & Music by Brian Wilson & Mike Love

Moderately

Green, Green Grass Of Home

Words & Music by Curly Putman

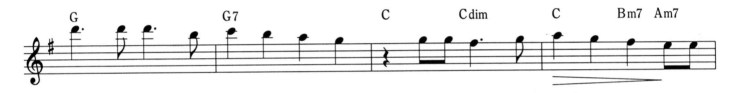

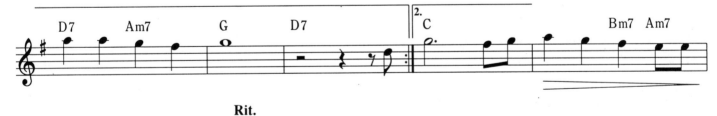

Release Me

Words & Music by Eddie Miller, Dub Williams, Robert Yount & Robert Harris

Somethin' Stupid

Words & Music by C. Carson Parks

Moderately slow

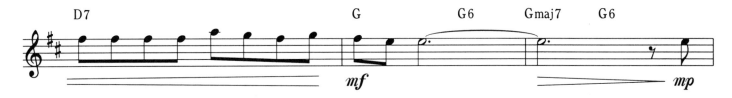

A Whiter Shade Of Pale

Words & Music by Keith Reid & Gary Brooker

Moderately, with feeling

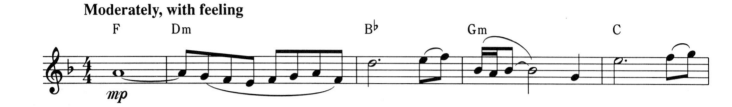

Massachusetts

Words & Music by Barry Gibb, Robin Gibb & Maurice Gibb

All You Need Is Love

Words & Music by John Lennon & Paul McCartney

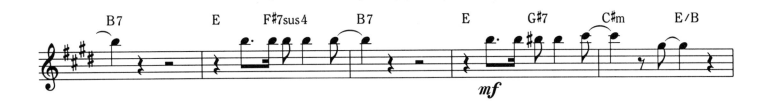

To Coda ⊕

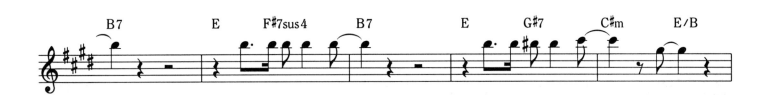

D.S. al Coda ⊕ Coda

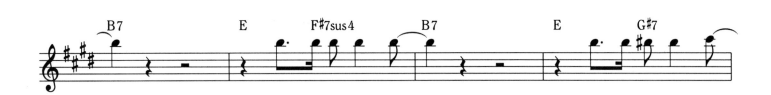

Repeat and Fade

Hello Goodbye

Words & Music by John Lennon & Paul McCartney

Lady Madonna

Words & Music by John Lennon & Paul McCartney

Jumpin' Jack Flash

Words & Music by Mick Jagger & Keith Richards

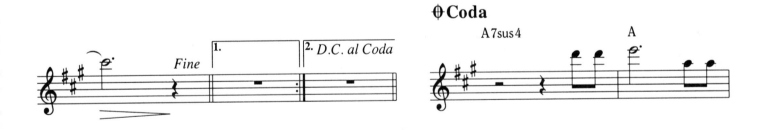

I've Got To Get
A Message To You

Words & Music by Barry Gibb, Robin Gibb & Maurice Gibb

Hey Jude

Words & Music by John Lennon & Paul McCartney

Those Were The Days

Words & Music by Gene Raskin

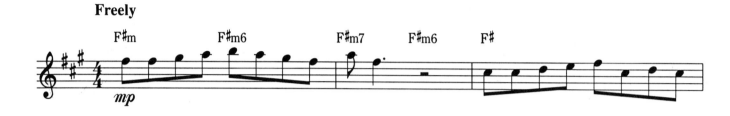

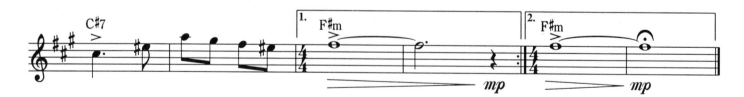

I'd Like To Teach The World To Sing

Words & Music by Roger Cook, Roger Greenaway, Billy Backer & Billy Davis

Ob-La-Di, Ob-La-Da

Words & Music by John Lennon & Paul McCartney

Bright tempo

Bridge Over Troubled Water

Words & Music by Paul Simon

Spirit In The Sky

Words & Music by Norman Greenbaum

Amazing Grace

Traditional adapted by Judy Collins

Tenderly (not too fast)

Welcome Home

Music by S. Beldone. French Words by Jean Dupré.
English lyrics by Bryan Blackburn

Clair

Words & Music by Raymond O'Sullivan

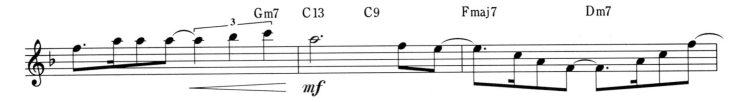

Rall. poco a poco

Tie A Yellow Ribbon
'Round The Ole Oak Tree

Words & Music by Irwin Levine & L. Russell Brown

Moderately bright

Annie's Song

Words & Music by John Denver

Whispering Grass

Words by Fred Fisher. Music by Doris Fisher

Merry Christmas Everybody

Words & Music by Neville Holder & James Lea

Gonna Make You A Star

Words & Music by David Essex

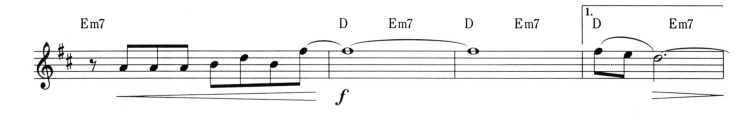

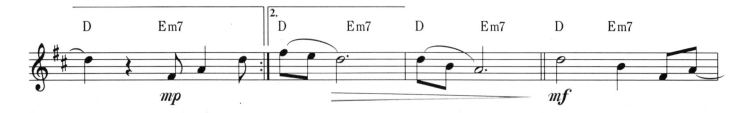

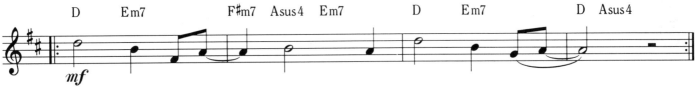

Sailing

Words & Music by Gavin Sutherland

Knowing Me, Knowing You

Words & Music by Benny Andersson, Stig Anderson & Bjorn Ulvaeus

I'm Not In Love

Words & Music by Eric Stewart & Graham Gouldman

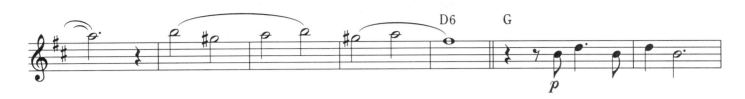

Mamma Mia

Words & Music by Benny Andersson, Stig Anderson & Bjorn Ulvaeus

Moderate steady four

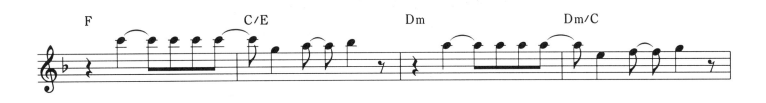

To Coda ⊕

1.

2.

⊕ Coda

D.S. al Coda

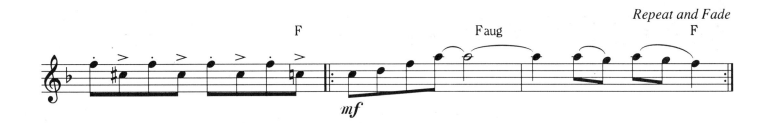

Repeat and Fade

mf

Fernando

Words & Music by Benny Andersson, Stig Anderson & Bjorn Ulvaeus

Moderate slow March

⊕ Coda

Dancing Queen

Words & Music by Benny Andersson, Stig Anderson & Bjorn Ulvaeus

Moderate Rock

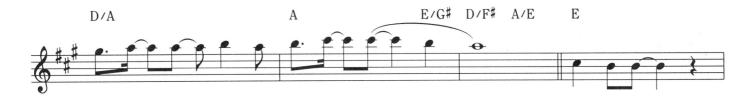

If You Leave Me Now

Words & Music by Peter Cetera

Moderately

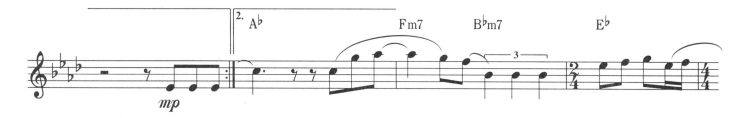

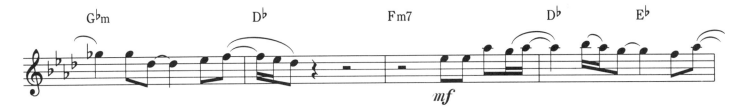

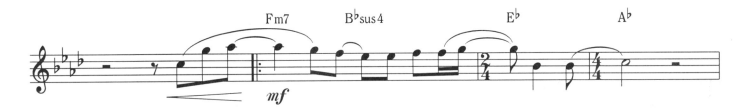

Don't Cry For Me Argentina

Music by Andrew Lloyd Webber. Lyrics by Tim Rice

poco rall   **Slow tango feel**

⊕**Coda**

YMCA

Words & Music by J. Morali, H. Belolo & V. Willis

Walking On The Moon

Words & Music by Sting

Mull Of Kintyre

Words & Music by McCartney & Laine

Moderately slow

Tragedy

Words & Music by Barry Gibb, Robin Gibb & Maurice Gibb

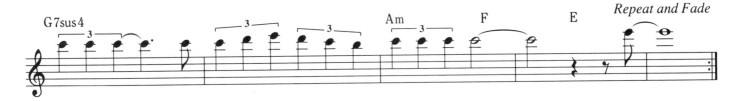

I Will Survive

Words & Music by Dino Fekaris & Freddie Perren

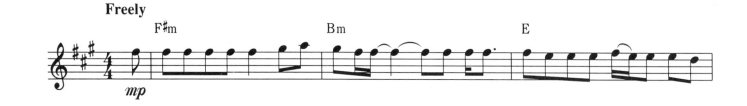

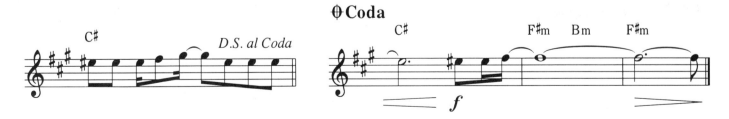

Bright Eyes

Words & Music by Mike Batt

Fairly slowly with expression

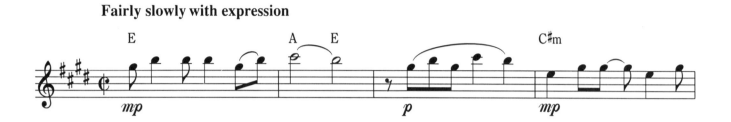

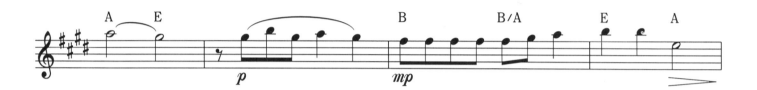

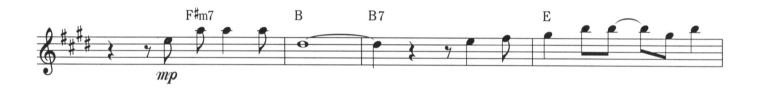

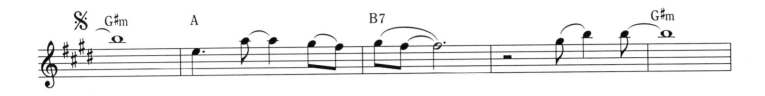

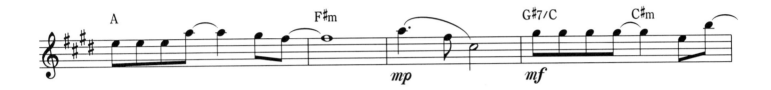

⊕Coda

We Don't Talk Anymore

Words & Music by Alan Tarney

Moderately

Message In A Bottle

Words & Music by Sting

Moderately fast

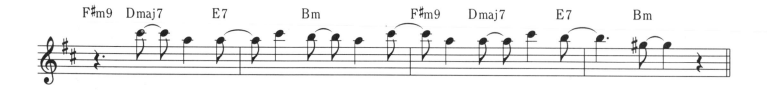

To Coda ⊕

D.C. al Coda

⊕ **Coda**

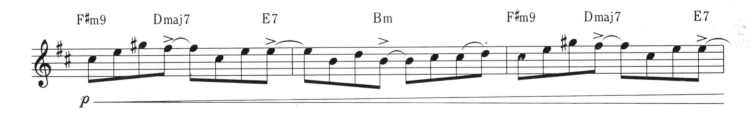

Repeat to Fade

What's Another Year

Words & Music by Shay Healy

Moderately

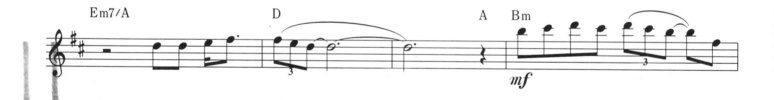

The Winner Takes It All

Words & Music by Benny Andersson & Bjorn Ulvaeus

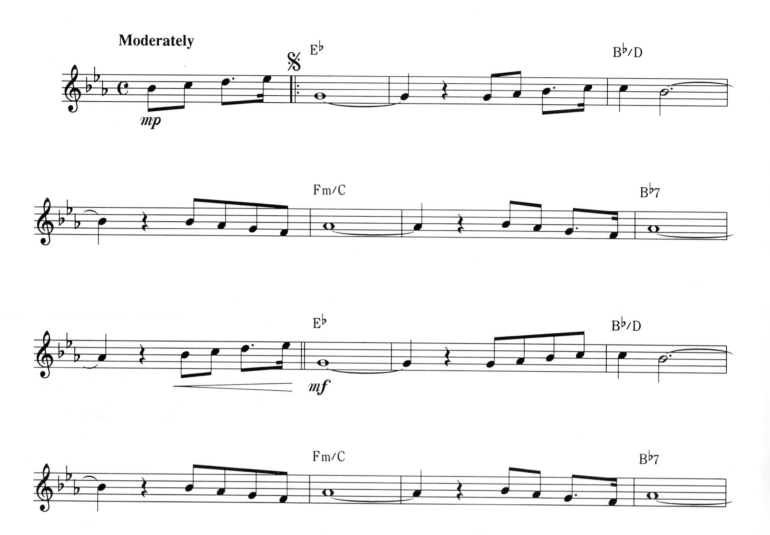

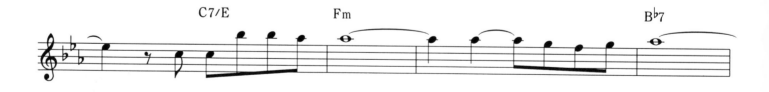

⊕ Coda

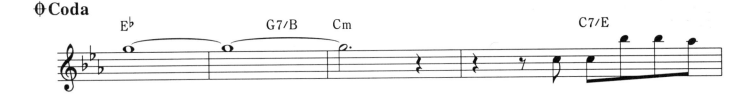

Don't Stand So Close To Me

Words & Music by Sting

A Woman In Love

Words & Music by Barry Gibb & Robin Gibb

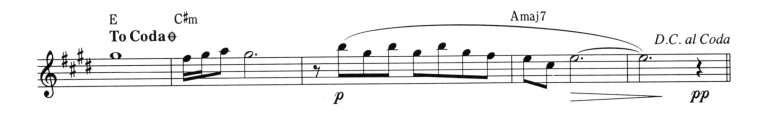

⊕ Coda

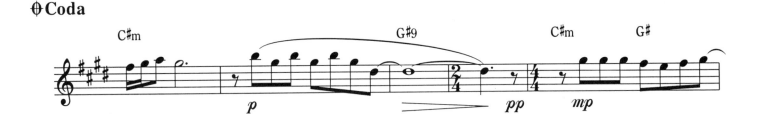

(Just Like) Starting Over

Words & Music by John Lennon

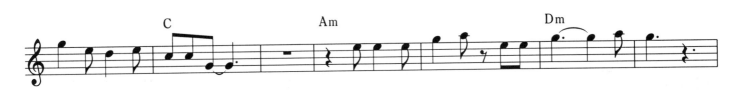

Imagine

Words & Music by John Lennon

Jealous Guy

Words & Music by John Lennon

Moderately slow

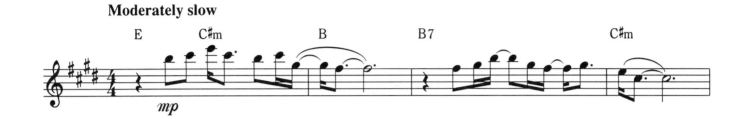

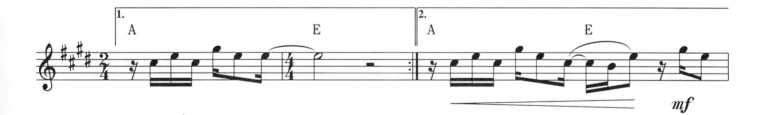

This Ole House

Words & Music by Stuart Hamblen

A Good Heart

Words & Music by Maria McKee

Moderately

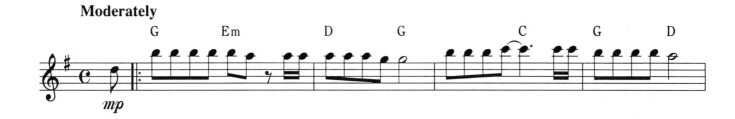

Ebony And Ivory

Words & Music by McCartney

Moderately

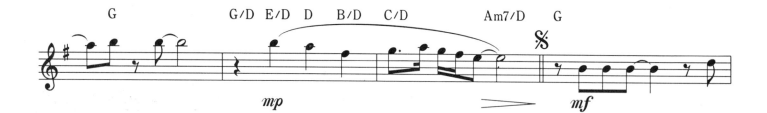

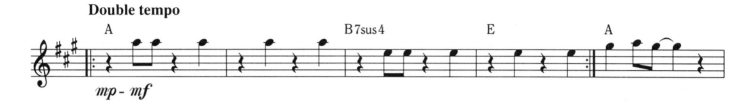

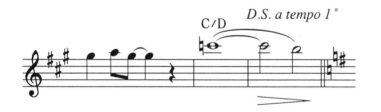

Save Your Love

Words & Music by John & Sue Edward

Moderately

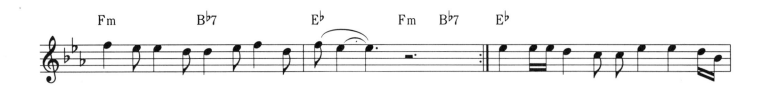

Every Breath You Take

Words & Music by Sting

Medium Rock

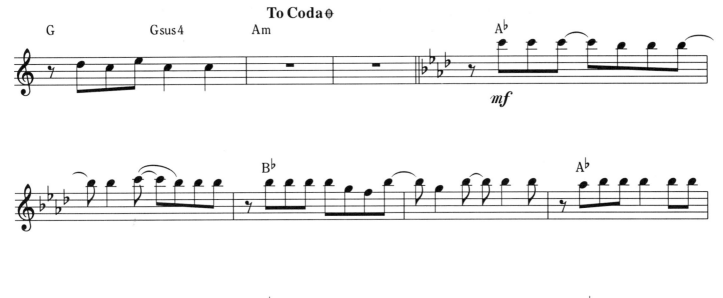

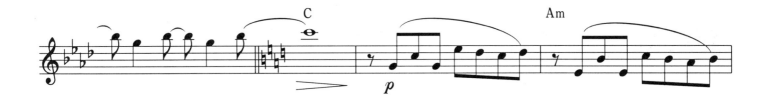

Pipes Of Peace

Words & Music by McCartney

Moderately

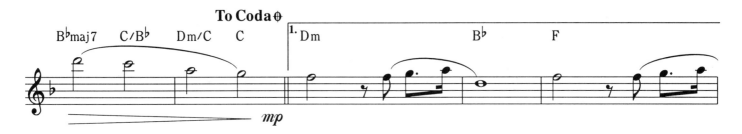

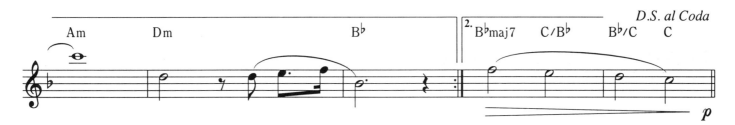

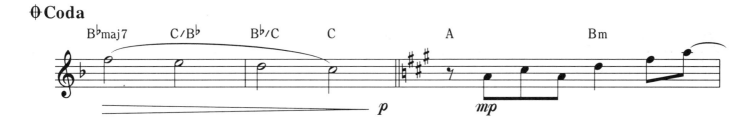

I Know Him So Well

Words & Music by Benny Andersson, Tim Rice & Bjorn Ulvaeus

Moderately

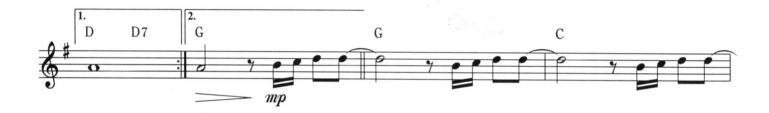

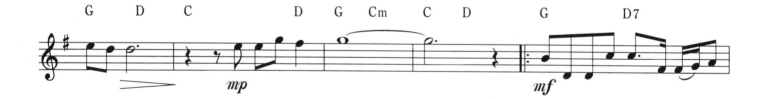

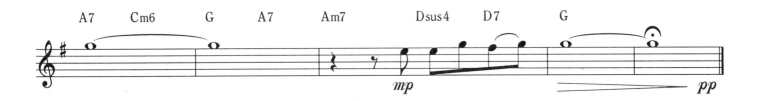

There Must Be An Angel
(Playing With My Heart)

Words & Music by A. Lennox & D. A. Stewart

The Power Of Love

Words & Music by C. de Rouge, G. Mende, J. Rush & S. Applegate

Moderately

121

Uptown Girl

Words & Music by Billy Joel

Moderato

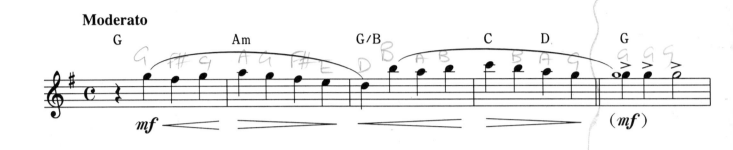

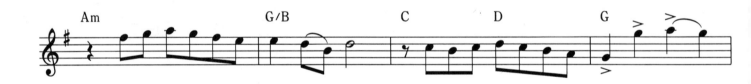

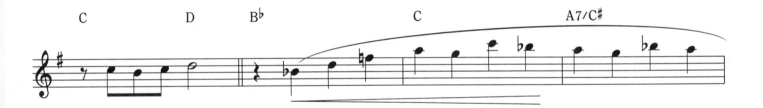

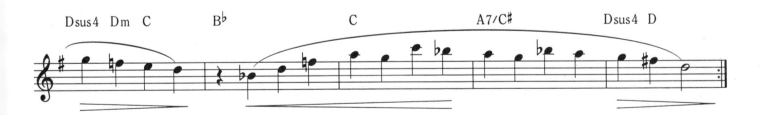

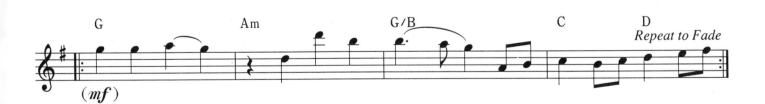

I Want To Wake Up With You

Words & Music by Ben Peters

Moderately

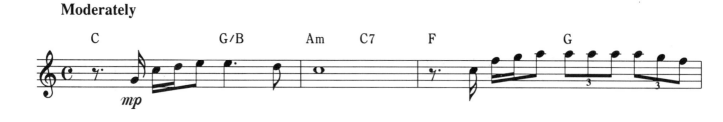

Always On My Mind

Words & Music by Wayne Thompson, Mark James & Johnny Christopher

When The Going Gets Tough, The Tough Get Going

Words & Music by Wayne Brathwaite, Barry Eastmond, R.J. Lange & Billy Ocean

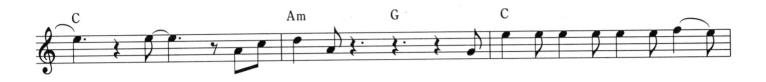

The Lady In Red

Words & Music by Chris De Burgh

Moderately

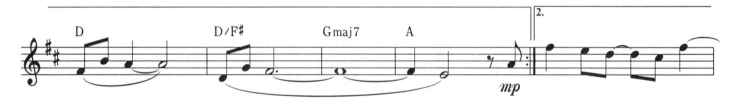

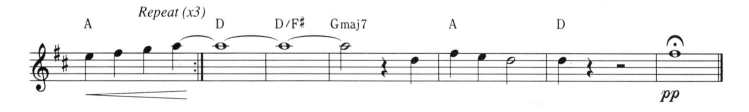

I Wanna Dance With Somebody
(Who Loves Me)

Words & Music by George Merrill & Shannon Rubicam

Moderately

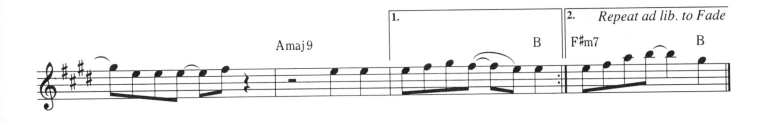

You Win Again

Words & Music by Barry Gibb, Robin Gibb & Maurice Gibb

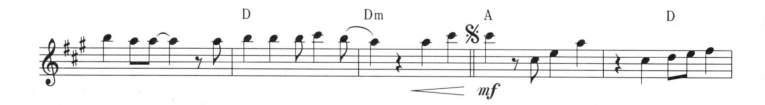

I Think We're Alone Now

Words & Music by Ritchie Cordell

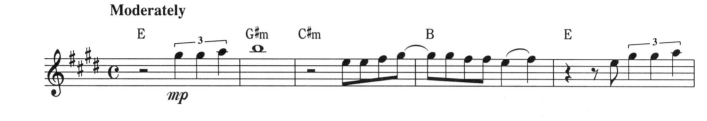

He Ain't Heavy He's My Brother

Mistletoe And Wine

Music by Keith Strachan. Words by Leslie Stewart & Jeremy Paul

Hangin' Tough

Words & Music by Maurice Starr

One Moment In Time

Words & Music by Albert Hammond & John Bettis

Moderately slow

3°continue

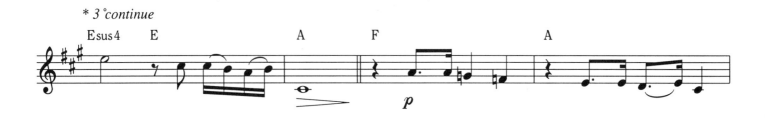

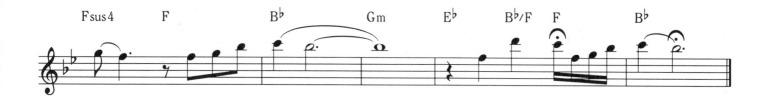

Something's Gotten Hold Of My Heart

Words & Music by Roger Cook & Roger Greenaway

Eternal Flame

Words & Music by Billy Steinberg, Tom Kelly & Susanna Hoffs

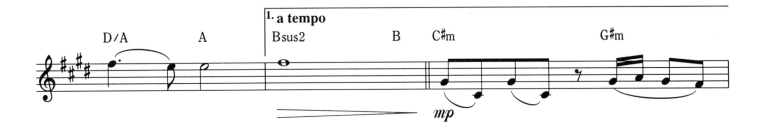

Itsy Bitsy, Teenie Weenie Yellow Polkadot Bikini

Words & Music by Lee Pockriss & Paul J. Vance

vocal cue: Two, three, four, tell the peo-ple what she wore.

vocal cue: Two, three, four, Stick a-round we'll tell you more.

Unchained Melody

Music by Alex North. Words by Hy Zaret.

Saviour's Day

Words & Music by Chris Eaton

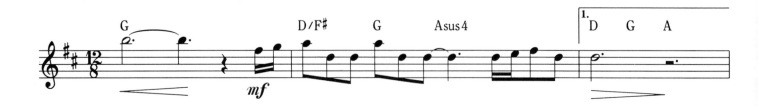

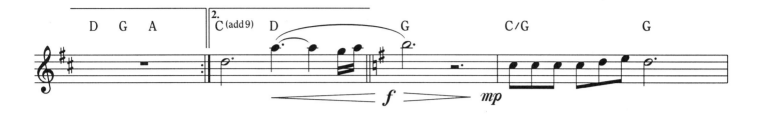

Repeat to Fade

(Everything I Do) I Do It For You

Words & Music by Bryan Adams, Michael Kamen & Robert John 'Mutt' Lange

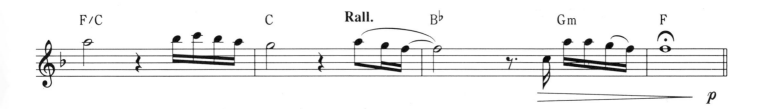

Goodnight Girl

Words & Music by Clarke, Cunningham, Mitchell & Pellow

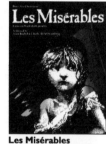

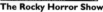